MACMILLAN READERS
ELEMENTARY LEVEL

JOHN MILNE

The Black Cat

MACMILLAN

MACMILLAN READERS

ELEMENTARY LEVEL

Founding Editor: John Milne

The Macmillan Readers provide a choice of enjoyable reading materials for learners of English. The series is published at six levels – Starter, Beginner, Elementary, Pre-intermediate, Intermediate and Upper.

Level control

Information, structure and vocabulary are controlled to suit the students' ability at each level.

The number of words at each level:

Starter	about 300 basic words
Beginner	about 600 basic words
Elementary	about 1100 basic words
Pre-intermediate	about 1400 basic words
Intermediate	about 1600 basic words
Upper	about 2200 basic words

Vocabulary

Some difficult words and phrases in this book are important for understanding the story. Some of these words are explained in the story and some are shown in the pictures. From Pre-intermediate level upwards, words are marked with a number like this: …[3]. These words are explained in the Glossary at the end of the book.

Contents

	Introductory Note	6
	The People in This Story	7
1	Salahadin is Worried	10
2	The Missing Box	12
3	The Taxi Driver	16
4	Boat to Beirut	20
5	The Black Cat	22
6	In Beirut	25
7	The Road to Ba'albek	28
8	Borkman's Story	31
9	Beirut to Athens	34
10	Salahadin finds Peterson	37
11	Salahadin finds the Black Cat	39
12	Death on *The Syria*	42
13	Do Not Disturb	45
14	Return to Cairo	48
15	The End	51
	Points for Understanding	55

The Black Cat

Introductory Note

The main character in this story is called Salahadin. He is an inspector in the Egyptian police. His job is to protect Egyptian antiquities. An antiquity is something which is very old.

There are many antiquities in Egypt. Most of them are valuable. Many of them are in museums in Cairo or in Europe. But there are many others which have not yet been found. These antiquities are buried under the sands, in tombs or in pyramids.

There are many archeologists working in Egypt. Archeologists study ancient cities and tombs. Sometimes they find antiquities. They must give all these antiquities to the Egyptian Government. But some archeologists try to keep them. Salahadin's job is to stop this happening.

Salahadin has studied history at Cairo University and at the University of London. He has visited many museums in Cairo and in Europe.

The People in This Story

Salahadin

Ahmed

Taxi driver

Fuad

Leila

Borkman

ARCHEOLOGIST MURDERED

Yesterday morning, an archeologist was found dead in a Cairo hotel.

The archeologist was called Pearson.

The police are making enquiries.

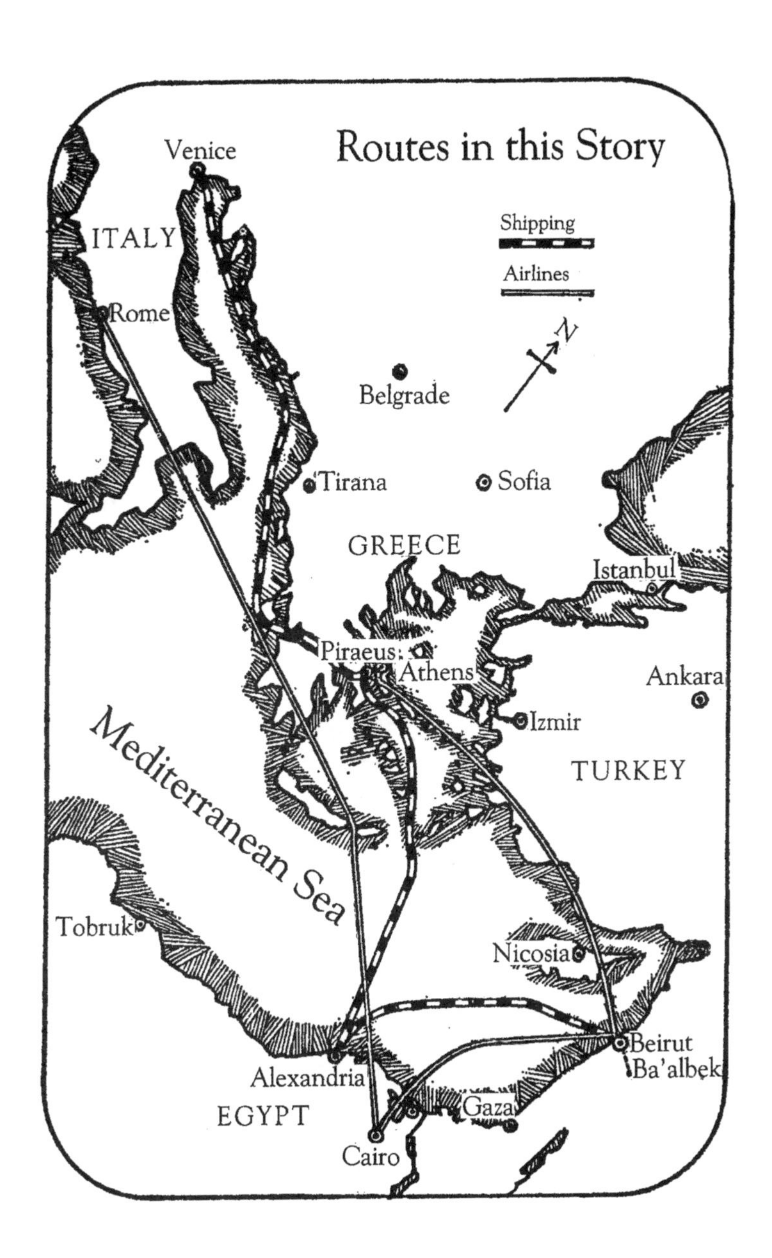
Routes in this Story
Shipping
Airlines
N
Venice
ITALY
Rome
Belgrade
Tirana
Sofia
GREECE
Istanbul
Piraeus
Athens
Ankara
Izmir
TURKEY
Mediterranean Sea
Tobruk
Nicosia
Beirut
Ba'albek
Alexandria
EGYPT
Gaza
Cairo

1

Salahadin is Worried

Salahadin was sitting in his office with his coat off. It was the month of May in Cairo and it was very hot. Salahadin stood up and turned on the fan. He was a young man, only twenty-eight years old. He was not very tall and quite thin. His black hair was cut very short.

Salahadin's office was in the centre of Cairo. It was in a large building behind the Nile Hotel. It was a small office and Salahadin's name was not on the door. Not many people knew that he was a detective. But he was not an ordinary detective. Inspector Salahadin protected all the antiquities of Egypt.

Salahadin was waiting for an archeologist called Mr Pearson. Pearson had been in Egypt for six months. He had been working in a valley in the south of Egypt. Pearson had been looking for antiquities. He had come back to Cairo a few days ago and was leaving Egypt soon.

But Mr Pearson had not come to Salahadin's office. Every archeologist had to see Salahadin before they left Egypt. Salahadin was worried. Pearson had not come yet.

Salahadin picked up the telephone and rang the number of Pearson's hotel.

'Nile Hotel,' said a voice. 'Can I help you?'

'Can I speak to the manager, please,' said Salahadin.

Salahadin waited for a few moments. Then he heard the manager's voice.

'Can I help you?' said the manager.

'Yes,' replied Salahadin. 'My name's Salahadin El Nur. I'm a police inspector. I want to speak to Mr Pearson.'

'Do you mean Mr Pearson, the archeologist?' asked the manager.

'Yes,' replied Salahadin.

'I'm sorry. You can't speak to Mr Pearson, sir,' said the manager.

'Oh,' said Salahadin in surprise. 'Why not?'

'Mr Pearson is dead,' replied the manager. 'He was found dead in his room this morning. Mr Pearson was murdered.'

2

The Missing Box

Salahadin put on his coat and quickly left his office. It was much hotter outside in the street. A hot, dusty wind was blowing between the tall buildings. Salahadin jumped into a taxi. The streets were full of cars and the taxi moved slowly. It took a long time to get to the Nile Hotel.

A policeman was standing at the door of the hotel.

'I'm sorry,' said the policeman. 'No one is allowed into the hotel.'

Salahadin showed the policeman his identity card.

The policeman took Salahadin to his chief. Luckily, Salahadin knew this officer. It was Inspector Ahmed, a school friend of Salahadin's.

Ahmed took Salahadin upstairs to Pearson's room. Pearson was lying on the bed. There was a knife in his chest.

'Why are you interested in this man?' Ahmed asked Salahadin. 'Do you know him?'

'His name is Pearson,' replied Salahadin. 'He's an archeologist. He was working in the south. He was leaving Egypt soon and I wanted to see him.'

'Why was he murdered?' Ahmed asked Salahadin.

'I don't know,' replied Salahadin.

There were some boxes standing against the wall. Salahadin pointed to them.

'Perhaps there's something valuable in these boxes,' said Salahadin. 'We must open them.'

Ahmed brought in two policemen and they started to open the boxes.

Salahadin looked carefully round the room. There were some papers on the table beside the bed. Salahadin picked them up. There was a map under the papers. On the map were the words, "Valley of Zar".

These may be important, thought Salahadin. I'll take them with me and look at them later.

Salahadin folded the papers and the map and put them carefully in his wallet.

By this time, the policemen had opened the boxes. There was nothing important in them. The boxes were full of spades and other things for digging.

'There's nothing important or valuable in these boxes,' said Salahadin. 'We must speak to all of the hotel staff. Perhaps one of them noticed something unusual.'

The manager brought the staff to Ahmed and Salahadin. They asked each person many questions, but they did not learn anything important.

Pearson's Map

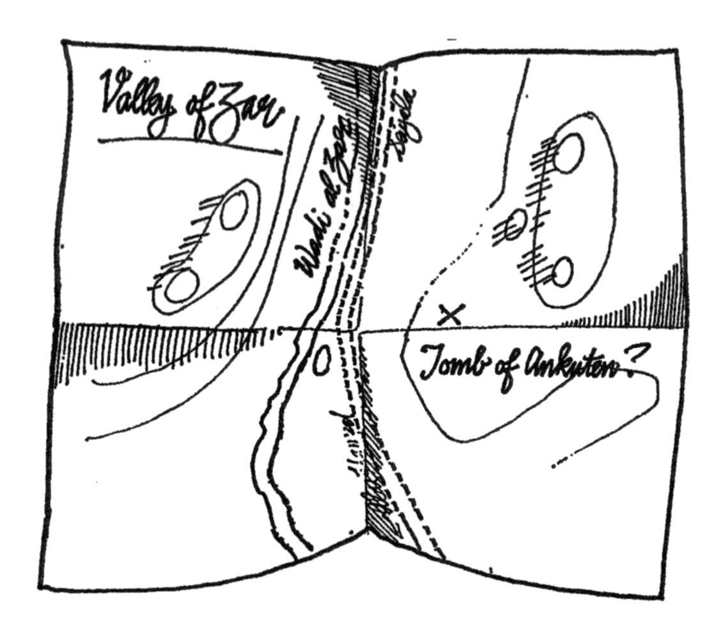

Then Salahadin had an idea.

'Who carried these boxes to this room?' he asked the manager.

The manager brought back two porters.

'Did you carry these boxes into this room?' Salahadin asked the porters.

'Yes,' they replied.

'How many boxes were there?' asked Salahadin.

'Six boxes,' replied the first porter. 'I carried three and my friend carried three.'

Salahadin looked at the boxes. There were six of them. No one had taken a box.

'Wait a moment,' said the second porter. 'You're wrong. There were seven boxes. You carried three, I carried three.'

'But that makes six boxes, not seven,' said Ahmed, with a smile. 'You can't count.'

'I can count,' replied the porter. 'There were seven boxes. Mr Pearson carried one into the room himself. It was a heavy box, but it was smaller than the others.'

'That is the box which is missing,' Salahadin said to Ahmed. 'There's something valuable in that seventh box. When we find the seventh box, we'll find the murderer.'

3

The Taxi Driver

Ahmed and Salahadin left Pearson's room and went down stairs. They sat down and the manager brought them some coffee.

'How can we find the seventh box?' asked Ahmed.

'I need your help,' replied Salahadin.

'How can I help you?' asked Ahmed.

'The murderer took the box with him,' said Salahadin. 'It was heavy and it's hot today. The murderer did not carry the box very far. Perhaps he took a taxi.'

'Perhaps he had his own car,' said Ahmed.

'We don't know,' replied Salahadin. 'But, perhaps he took a taxi.'

'That's possible,' agreed Ahmed. 'And you want to find that taxi. But, how can I help you?'

'You can send out a police message on Radio Cairo,' replied Salahadin.

'That's true,' agreed Ahmed. 'What shall I say in the message?'

'When did Pearson die?' asked Salahadin.

'About half past ten this morning,' replied Ahmed.

'Then here's the message,' said Salahadin. 'The police want to speak to a taxi driver. This taxi driver was near the Nile Hotel at about eleven o'clock this morning. A man got into his taxi. The man was carrying a heavy box. The police want to speak to the taxi driver as soon as possible.'

'Good,' said Ahmed. 'I'll put out this message immediately.'

'Most taxis have radios,' said Salahadin. 'Perhaps a taxi

driver will remember a man with a heavy box.

'I'll get back to my office,' went on Salahadin. 'When anything happens, let me know.'

'I'll telephone you immediately,' replied Ahmed.

It was now late afternoon. Outside on the street it was still very hot. Salahadin got into a taxi. Luckily there were few cars and the streets were almost empty. He soon arrived back in his office.

Salahadin turned on the radio. He heard the message. It was repeated after fifteen minutes. Salahadin waited. Suddenly the telephone rang. It was Ahmed.

'We've been lucky,' said Ahmed. 'A taxi driver is here in my office. A man with a heavy box got into his taxi near the Nile Hotel.'

'At what time?' asked Salahadin.

'At eleven o'clock this morning,' replied Ahmed. 'Do you want to speak to him?'

'Certainly,' replied Salahadin. 'I'll come round to your office immediately.'

Ahmed's office was quite near. Salahadin walked there. The sun had gone down and it was becoming cooler.

The taxi driver was waiting in Ahmed's office. He was a fat, happy-looking man. He was also intelligent. Salahadin took out his notebook and asked the taxi driver some questions.

'At what time did this man get into your taxi?' asked Salahadin.

'A few minutes before eleven o'clock,' replied the taxi driver. 'He got in quite near the Nile Hotel.'

'Was he carrying anything?' Salahadin asked.

'Yes,' replied the taxi driver, 'a heavy box.'

'And what did he look like?' asked Salahadin.

'He was tall with broad shoulders,' replied the taxi driver. 'He had fair hair. He spoke Arabic, but he was not an Arab. Perhaps he was Swedish.'

Salahadin thought for a few moments. Then he asked the taxi driver another question.

'This man spoke Arabic, did he?' asked Salahadin. 'What kind of Arabic did he speak?'

'What do you mean?' asked the driver.

'Did he speak Arabic like an Egyptian?' asked Salahadin.

'Oh, no,' said the taxi driver. 'He spoke like a Lebanese.'

'Where did you take this man?' said Salahadin, continuing his questions.

'I took him to the railway station,' replied the driver. 'He wanted to get there before twelve o'clock.'

'Twelve o'clock, midday,' said Salahadin quietly. 'What train leaves Cairo at twelve o'clock?'

'The express train for Alexandria,' said the taxi driver immediately. 'I know all the trains. The express train leaves Cairo at twelve o'clock and arrives in Alexandria at half past two.'

Salahadin had been lucky. He had found out some important facts. He looked at the notes in his book.

Pearson's murderer?   X?

What does he look like?

tall and broad

fair hair

perhaps X is Swedish?

Where is X going?

went to Cairo Railway Station

before twelve o'clock

train leaves for Alexandria

at twelve o'clock.

Perhaps X is going to Alexandria

Why Alexandria?

Alexandria – Beirut??

بيروت?

many ships go from Alexandria

to Beirut

easy to get a heavy box on a boat –

not so easy to get a box on an aeroplane

Remember X speaks Arabic like a Lebanese!

Perhaps X is going to take a boat to Beirut?

4

Boat to Beirut

It was now after seven o'clock in the evening. The train from Cairo had arrived at Alexandria at half past two. Perhaps Pearson's murderer was already on a boat to Beirut.

'We must phone Alexandria,' said Salahadin to Ahmed.

Salahadin picked up the telephone. He asked for the police at the docks in Alexandria. After about ten minutes, the telephone rang. It was the call to Alexandria.

'This is Salahadin El Nur speaking. I'm a police inspector and I want to speak to your chief.'

The chief of the dock police came to the telephone. Salahadin asked some questions and wrote the answers down in his notebook. Here are his notes.

A tall man with fair hair arrived at the docks at six o'clock.
Man was carrying a heavy box.
He had a Swedish passport.
All the papers already sent to Cairo.
Man said the box was full of books.
Box was not opened – police do not open every box.

Two boats had left Alexandria after
4.30 pm.
A boat left at half past six for Beirut.
Its name – The Sudan.
Another boat left for Athens at 7pm.
Its name – The Syria.

Man said he was going to Beirut.
The police did not see him getting
on the boat for Beirut.

Salahadin put down the telephone and looked at his notes for some time. Then he spoke to Ahmed.

'Pearson's murderer has gone to Beirut,' he said. 'I'm sure of that.'

'Then we can send a message to the boat,' said Ahmed.

'No, we won't do that,' said Salahadin. 'We're not really certain. Many men have fair hair and many men carry heavy boxes. I must meet him. I must speak to him.'

'But how can you do that?' asked Ahmed. 'It's too late now. The boat has already left.'

'I can get to Beirut before him,' replied Salahadin. 'Today is Monday. The boat won't be in Beirut until tomorrow evening. I can take an aeroplane.'

'And the plane takes only two hours,' said Ahmed.

'That's right,' said Salahadin. 'I'll take a plane tomorrow morning and I'll be in Beirut before midday.'

'That's a good idea,' said Ahmed. 'You can meet this man on the docks at Beirut.'

'And now I must go. I've a lot to do,' said Salahadin. 'I must book a seat on the aeroplane and get a ticket. I'll see you later. Thanks for your help. Goodbye.'

5

The Black Cat

Salahadin got home very late. It was nearly midnight and he was very tired. But his work was not yet finished. He took some pieces of paper out of his wallet. They were the pieces of paper from Pearson's room. Salahadin sat down and looked at Pearson's notes.

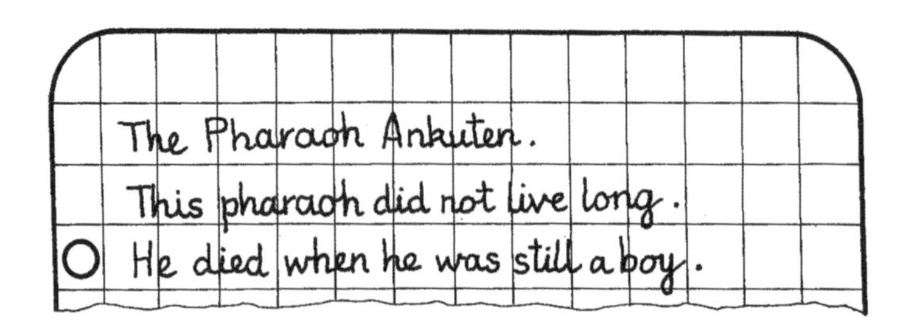
The Pharaoh Ankuten.
This pharaoh did not live long.
He died when he was still a boy.

Where was Ankuten buried?

Ankuten was going to the Sudan when he died.
The Valley of Zar is beside the road to the Sudan.
Was Ankuten buried in the Valley of Zar?

What was buried with Ankuten in his tomb?

Was there a cat buried with Ankuten?
There are many old stories about a black cat.
Ankuten loved black cats.
When he died, a black cat was put in his tomb.
But this cat was very unusual.
It was made of gold. Its eyes were diamonds.
There was a collar of diamonds round
its neck.
Is this story true or not?

Why was the cat covered with black paint?

Fear of robbers.
Black paint hid the gold and diamonds.
A cat painted in thick black paint did not

look valuable.

Questions that must be answered:

- Is Ankuten buried in the Valley of Zar?
- Is there a black cat in his tomb?
- Is the black cat made of gold?
- Or is it made of wood?
- Are the stories true or false?

Salahadin read the notes again. He asked himself some questions. Did Pearson find the tomb of Ankuten? he asked himself. Did he find a black cat? And is the black cat made of gold?

There was a reason for Pearson's death. Was the Black Cat the reason?

There are too many questions, thought Salahadin. I must find some answers. The answers are in the missing box and it's probably on its way to Beirut. I'll be there tomorrow.

6

In Beirut

At half past ten the next morning, Salahadin arrived at Beirut airport. The airport lies to the south of the city and the docks are in the north. One road from the airport to the docks goes through the centre of the city. Another road goes beside the sea.

Salahadin got into a taxi. He told the driver to take the road beside the sea. The sun was shining on the city and there was a mist on the hills behind. The air was fresh and cool. Salahadin felt very happy in Beirut. It was nice and cool after the heat and dust of Cairo.

When he got to the docks, he asked about the boat from Alexandria. *The Sudan* did not arrive at Beirut until half past six in the evening. Salahadin had more than six hours to wait. He decided to visit a friend called Fuad.

Fuad had been a student with Salahadin at Cairo University. He now worked in the Lebanese Department of Antiquities in Beirut. His office was in a large museum in the north-east part of the city. Salahadin took a taxi to the museum.

Fuad was surprised and pleased to see him.

'We'll have lunch together,' said Fuad. 'I'll phone my wife immediately.'

Ten minutes later they were in Fuad's car. Fuad lived in a small village in the mountains above Beirut. The road was very steep. It twisted and turned up the mountain.

'This road is dangerous,' said Salahadin.

'You're right,' replied Fuad. 'And it's more dangerous higher up. People are often killed up there.'

The road was very steep. It twisted and turned up the mountain.

But it was also very beautiful. It was spring and the trees and the flowers were fresh and green. Some people were already selling fruit beside the road. They had large baskets of strawberries.

The car soon arrived at Fuad's house. Fuad's wife, Leila, was waiting for them.

'Hello, Salahadin,' said Leila. 'It's nice to see you again. We've a lot to talk about. But first, we'll have lunch.'

After lunch they sat out on the verandah and drank coffee. They talked about Cairo and their friends there. From the verandah, they looked down towards the tall buildings of Beirut. Behind the buildings were the docks and the sea.

'Now,' said Fuad, 'why are you in Beirut?'

Salahadin told Fuad about the death of Pearson. He told him, also, about the man with fair hair.

'I want to be at the docks at six o'clock,' said Salahadin. 'I'm going to meet *The Sudan*. It arrives at half past six.'

'I'll take you there in my car,' said Fuad.

They sat on the verandah and talked together. The time passed quickly and soon they had to leave for the docks.

'Bring Salahadin back here,' Leila said to Fuad. 'Our house is more comfortable than a hotel. He must stay here tonight.'

Salahadin thanked Leila and stood up.

'It's getting cold,' he said.

'Yes,' replied Fuad. 'You're wearing summer clothes. This is not Cairo. It's cold here in the mountains. It's cold sometimes even in summer. I'll get you a warm coat. You'll need it later.'

At five o'clock, Salahadin and Fuad left the house. They said goodbye to Leila and drove down the steep road towards Beirut.

7

The Road to Ba'albek

At six o'clock, Salahadin and Fuad arrived at the docks in Beirut. They sat in the car and waited for the arrival of *The Sudan*.

There was another car on the docks.

'Do you see that black car over there?' asked Fuad.

'The one with two men in the front?'

'Yes,' said Fuad, 'and there's a fat man sitting in the back seat. I know him. He's interested in antiquities. He often comes to the museum.'

The Sudan soon appeared at the entrance to the docks. It reached the dockside just after half past six and the passengers came down the gangway.

'There he is,' said Salahadin, 'the man on the gangway! He's tall. He has fair hair and broad shoulders. That's the man.'

'But, I know him,' said Fuad. 'He's a Swede and his name is Borkman. He's interested in antiquities, too. I've often seen him in the museum.'

'Where's the box?' asked Salahadin. 'He's not carrying a box.'

'Let's wait and see,' said Fuad. 'Perhaps he's given the box to a porter.'

'Look,' said Salahadin. 'The black car is moving.'

The black car moved a few metres and stopped again behind a shed. Fuad and Salahadin sat and waited. Borkman got off the boat and got into a taxi. But he was not carrying a heavy box. The taxi started to move away.

'Let's follow him,' said Fuad.

'There he is,' said Salahadin, 'the man on the gangway!'

'Wait a moment,' said Salahadin. 'Watch the black car.'

Salahadin was right. The black car pulled out slowly and followed Borkman's taxi.

'We can go now,' said Salahadin. 'We'll follow the black car. There's something strange here.'

The three cars drove out of the docks, one after the other. The taxi went quickly through the streets of Beirut. Then it started to climb the steep road towards the mountains. The black car followed the taxi. Fuad followed the black car.

'Isn't this the road to your village?' asked Salahadin.

'Yes,' replied Fuad. 'This road goes higher up the mountains. It goes to a small town called Ba'albek.'

'I've heard of Ba'albek,' said Salahadin. 'There are some famous ruins there.'

'And there's a gang of smugglers, too,' said Fuad. 'They smuggle antiquities out of Beirut.'

The three cars drove up the steep road. They went past Fuad's village. Fuad drove on in silence. The road became narrower and steeper and Fuad did not drive too close to the black car.

'The road's more dangerous here,' said Fuad. 'There was an accident a few weeks ago. Four people were killed.'

For a few moments nothing happened. Then the black car began to go faster. It had moved into the middle of the road and was trying to pass Borkman's taxi. The two cars were now side by side. They were almost touching each other.

There was a sharp bend in the road in front of them.

'They'll never get round that bend,' shouted Fuad.

But it was already too late. There was a loud crashing noise. Fuad slowed down and drove carefully round the bend. The black car and the taxi had disappeared. In front of them, the road was empty. Everything was silent.

8

Borkman's Story

Fuad and Salahadin got out of the car and walked to the edge of the road. It was now getting dark and cold. The two cars lay below them. The black car had fallen about two hundred metres to the bottom. It was on fire. The taxi had not fallen so far. It was lying against a tree.

'Come on,' said Salahadin. 'Let's climb down quickly. Perhaps Borkman's still alive.'

Fuad climbed down the steep path and Salahadin followed him. They found the taxi. The driver was inside, but he was dead. One of the doors was open and Borkman had fallen out onto some bushes. He was not dead, but he was badly injured.

Fuad bent down and lifted the dying man. He laid him on a flat piece of ground. After a few moments, Borkman opened his eyes and looked up. He tried to speak, but he did not speak very clearly.

'The men in the black car ...' he said. 'Where are they? What happened to them?'

'They're dead,' replied Salahadin quietly.

'But who are you?' asked Borkman.

'We were passing on the road,' replied Fuad. 'We saw the accident.'

There was silence for a few moments. Borkman closed his eyes and lay still on the ground. Then he slowly opened his eyes again.

'Will you help me?' he asked.

'Yes,' replied Fuad. 'What do you want?'

'Go to Ba'albek,' said Borkman. 'Go to Jusef's café. Ask

The black car had fallen about two hundred metres to the bottom. It was on fire.

for Jusef. Tell Jusef ...'

Borkman was silent again.

'What do I tell Jusef?' asked Fuad.

'Tell him that Pearson's dead,' said Borkman. 'And the Black Cat's safe.'

'Where is the Black Cat?' asked Salahadin.

'Tell Jusef that the Black Cat's safe,' said Borkman again.

'But where is it?' asked Salahadin again.

'Peterson has the Black Cat,' said Borkman after a few moments. 'I gave it to him at Alexandria. He took it with him on the boat.'

'Which boat?' asked Salahadin.

'The boat to Athens,' replied Borkman. 'Peterson took the Black Cat on the boat to Athens.'

'Who was following you then?' asked Fuad.

'The Red Hand Gang,' replied Borkman. 'They wanted the Black Cat. But the Black Cat is safe. Tell Jusef ... Tell Jusef ...'

Borkman closed his eyes for the last time. Blood was running out of his mouth and his body shook strongly for a moment. Then he lay still. He was dead.

'Let's get away quickly,' said Salahadin. 'I don't want to wait for the police. They'll take us with them to Ba'albek. I must leave Beirut immediately. I'm going to Athens. You can tell the police about this in the morning.'

Fuad and Salahadin climbed back up to the road. Some cars had stopped and people were looking down at the burning car. Fuad and Salahadin drove off quickly.

9

Beirut to Athens

Salahadin and Fuad got back home before ten o'clock. Leila was pleased to see them. She started to make some food, but Salahadin was in a hurry.

'Can you phone Beirut airport?' he asked Fuad. 'Find out the time of the first plane to Athens. I want to get there as soon as possible.'

Fuad phoned the airport. Leila brought in some coffee and they sat down. Salahadin told her about Borkman's death. He spoke about the Black Cat.

'But what is the Black Cat?' asked Leila.

Salahadin told her about the pharaoh Ankuten and about the tomb in the Valley of Zar.

'I know now that Pearson found the tomb,' said Salahadin. 'He found the cat in the tomb and brought it to Cairo. Pearson told Borkman about the cat. But Borkman was a member of the Ba'albek Gang. Pearson didn't know that. Borkman murdered Pearson and took the cat.'

'And where is the cat now?' asked Leila.

'Borkman had a plan,' replied Salahadin. 'He was not taking the cat to Beirut. He gave the cat to another man on the docks at Alexandria. This other man is called Peterson. Peterson has taken the Black Cat with him to Athens.'

While Salahadin was talking, he was making some notes in his book. This is what he wrote:

THE BLACK CAT

PEARSON
found Black Cat
took it to Cairo
told Borkman
Pearson murdered by Borkman

BORKMAN
took Black Cat to Alexandria
gave it to Peterson
came to Beirut
killed on road to Ba'albek

THE RED HAND GANG
heard about Black Cat
tried to stop Borkman
killed on road to Ba'albek

JUSEF
in café at Ba'albek
? leader of Ba'albek Gang

PETERSON
has Black Cat
is on a boat going to Athens
boat is called "The Syria"

Fuad came back from the telephone.

'There's a plane in four hours' time,' he said. 'It leaves Beirut at one o'clock in the morning and arrives in Athens at five.'

'How long does the boat take from Alexandria to Athens?' asked Salahadin.

'Almost two days,' replied Leila. 'I once went by boat on a holiday to Athens.'

'*The Syria* left Alexandria on Monday evening,' said Salahadin. 'It's Tuesday today. It won't arrive in Athens until tomorrow. I'll be in Athens before the boat.'

'We must leave soon,' said Fuad. 'It's a long way to the airport.'

Salahadin said goodbye to Leila and drove off with Fuad. They arrived at the airport just after midnight. It was already Wednesday. But Salahadin was only a few hours away from Athens by air. Salahadin thanked Fuad.

'Take care,' said Fuad. 'Six people have already died because of this Black Cat. Send us a telegram from Athens.'

'I'll send you a telegram from Athens tomorrow,' said Salahadin. Then he smiled. 'I mean today. It's Wednesday already. You go to the police in the morning. Tell them about Jusef's cafe.'

Salahadin said goodbye to Fuad and went to catch the plane for Athens.

10

Salahadin finds Peterson

Salahadin's plane flew over Athens early in the morning. From the aeroplane he looked down on the ruins of the Acropolis. They looked wonderful in the early morning sunlight. But Salahadin was not a tourist. He was a detective and he had to find Peterson.

Salahadin took a taxi from the airport to Piraeus, the seaport of Athens. He got out of the taxi at Piraeus and went to an office at the dock gate.

'What time does *The Syria* arrive from Alexandria?' he asked.

'At midday,' was the reply. 'And it leaves again for Venice at four o'clock.'

It was only six o'clock in the morning. Salahadin had a long time to wait. But Piraeus is full of small cafés and restaurants. Salahadin passed the time drinking coffee and sleeping.

At eleven o'clock Salahadin walked back to the docks. He tried to walk through the gate, but a policeman stopped him.

'You can't go through the gate without a ticket,' said the policeman.

Salahadin had an idea. The man in the office had said that *The Syria* was going to Venice. Salahadin went back to the office and bought a first class ticket to Venice.

When he got into the docks, *The Syria* had not yet arrived. Salahadin sat down on a box and waited.

'Peterson is not an Egyptian name,' thought Salahadin. 'It's another Swedish name, like Borkman. Perhaps

Peterson is Swedish also. I'll look for a man with fair hair. He'll be carrying a box.'

The Syria was half an hour late. It arrived in the docks at half past twelve. Salahadin watched the people getting off the boat. They were all Egyptian. There were some men with their wives and children, and many students. There was no one who looked Swedish.

At that moment, someone appeared on the top deck of *The Syria*. He was a tall man with fair hair.

That's Peterson, thought Salahadin. So, he's decided to stay on the boat. Perhaps he's going to Venice. I'll get on the boat and go to Venice, too.

But Salahadin was careful. Perhaps it was a trick and Peterson was going to get off the boat at the last moment. Salahadin waited, but no one else got off. At five o'clock, Salahadin got on the boat. The gangway was taken down and *The Syria* was ready to leave.

Salahadin went to the ticket office on the boat and showed his ticket to the officer.

'I've just got on the boat,' said Salahadin. 'Can I have a cabin, please?'

'You're travelling first class, sir,' the officer said. 'You can go into cabin 22. It's just under the top deck.'

The officer turned to get the key for cabin 22.

'Wait a moment, sir,' said the officer. 'I'm sorry. I've made a mistake. Cabin 22 isn't empty. Mr Peterson's in cabin 22. He's decided to go on to Venice. But cabin 23 is empty. You can go there.'

Salahadin took the key from the officer, went to cabin 23 and sat down. He had found Peterson.

11

Salahadin finds the Black Cat

Ten minutes later, there was a knock at the door of Salahadin's cabin. It was the steward.

'Do you want to eat in the dining-room or in your cabin, sir?' asked the steward.

'Where do people usually eat?' asked Salahadin.

'In the dining-room,' replied the steward. 'But you can have your dinner in your cabin, if you want.'

'That's an idea,' said Salahadin. 'I'll eat here.'

'I'll bring you dinner at eight o'clock then,' said the steward, and walked down the corridor.

Salahadin watched the steward carefully. The steward walked to a small room under the stairs.

Salahadin took out his notebook and drew a plan of the corridor and the cabins. Here is the plan:

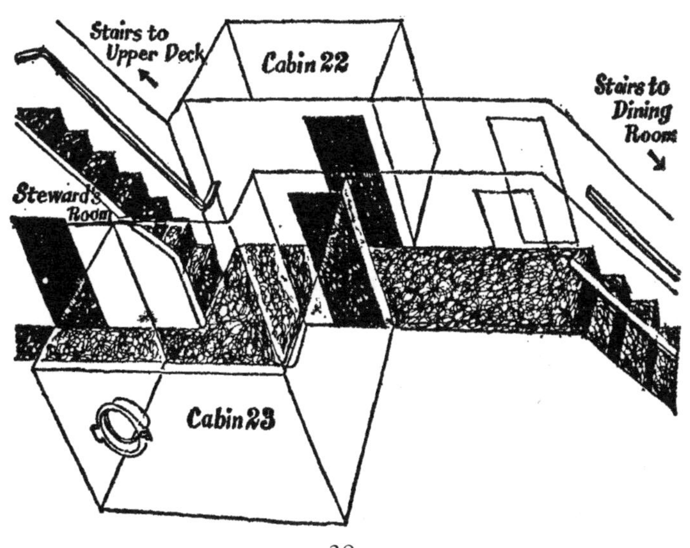

After a few moments, the steward came out of his room and walked down the corridor. Salahadin waited for five minutes. Everything was quiet in the corridor. Salahadin left his cabin and walked quietly to the steward's room under the stairs.

The steward had not locked the door. Salahadin opened it carefully and looked in. The room was small, with brushes and cleaning things in it. There were some hooks on the wall. A key hung from every hook and there was a number above each one.

Salahadin took the key of cabin 22 and went to the door. Suddenly he heard a noise. Peterson had come back. He was standing at the door of his cabin. Salahadin waited in the steward's room. Peterson went into his cabin and closed the door.

Salahadin quietly went back to his own cabin, sat down and listened. There was the noise of music. Peterson had turned on a radio. Then there was the noise of running water. Peterson was having a shower.

Salahadin had a shower, too, got dressed and waited. A few minutes later there was a knock at his door. The steward had brought Salahadin's dinner. At the same time, Peterson came out of his cabin. He locked the door and walked down the corridor. Peterson was going to the dining-room.

The steward went away and Salahadin was left alone. He looked out into the corridor. Everything was quiet. Salahadin left his cabin and crossed the corridor. He put the key in the lock of cabin 22 and quietly opened the door. Then he went into the cabin and shut the door carefully behind him.

Salahadin looked round the cabin. There was a case on

top of the cupboard and some clothes on the bed. But he did not see a box. He looked inside the shower-room. It was empty.

The Black Cat must be here, thought Salahadin. Where has he hidden it?

Then he had an idea. The shower-room was very high. Salahadin looked up. There was a box placed above the shower.

Salahadin lifted the box down on the bed and started to open it. But something had gone wrong. There was a noise and the door of cabin 22 suddenly opened. There was a man in the doorway. It was Peterson and he had a gun in his hand. The gun was pointing at Salahadin.

12

Death on *The Syria*

'Don't move,' said Peterson.

Peterson came into the cabin and shut the door. Salahadin stood still in front of the bed.

'Who are you?' asked Peterson. 'And what are you doing in my cabin?'

Salahadin thought quickly. He had to say something.

'Borkman sent me,' he said. 'I have a message for you.'

'You're telling lies,' said Peterson. 'There's something on the bed. Stand back.'

Salahadin moved back and Peterson saw the open box. 'So, you've found the Black Cat,' said Peterson. 'You're a member of the Red Hand Gang.'

Peterson opened the door and looked out into the corridor. It was empty.

'Put your hands behind your back and come out of the cabin,' said Peterson. 'Then walk slowly up the stairs to the top deck.'

Salahadin came out of the cabin and Peterson followed him. Salahadin walked slowly up the stairs.

When they reached the top deck, Peterson spoke again.

'Walk over to the rail.'

There was a rail round the side of the ship. Over the rail was the sea. *The Syria* had now passed through the Corinth Canal and the ship was rolling from side to side.

Salahadin walked slowly forward towards the funnel.

'Stop,' said Peterson. 'Turn round.'

Salahadin turned and looked at Peterson.

'Now, tell me the truth,' said Peterson. 'Who are you?'

Salahadin decided to tell some truth and some lies.

'Borkman's dead,' said Salahadin. 'And Jusef is caught. The Ba'albek Gang is finished. The police are waiting for you at Venice.'

'I don't believe you,' said Peterson. 'How do you know this? Who are you?'

'I'm an inspector in the Egyptian police,' replied Salahadin. 'I've followed you from Beirut. The Italian police are waiting for you at Venice.'

'You're telling lies again,' said Peterson. 'Why didn't you bring the police onto the boat at Athens?'

Salahadin did not reply and Peterson started to laugh.

'You didn't tell anyone at Athens,' he said. 'There's no one waiting for this boat at Venice. Now I'm going to shoot you. I'll throw your body into the sea and no one will ever know.'

Suddenly Peterson lifted his gun. At the same moment, a large wave shook the side of the ship. Peterson was thrown against the rail and the gun fell onto the deck. For a second, both men looked at the gun, then at each other. The wind pressed hard against them. Neither of them moved forward.

Peterson was the first to move. He tried to pick up the gun and Salahadin ran straight at him. He held Peterson round the neck and pushed him over the rail. Peterson fell backwards over the rail and disappeared into the angry sea below. There was a scream. Then there was silence.

Salahadin walked slowly away from the rail and sat down on the deck. No one came. Everyone was busy eating dinner. No one had heard the noise.

He held Peterson round the neck and pushed him over the rail.

13

Do Not Disturb

The corridor outside cabin 22 was still empty. Everything was silent. Salahadin went into the cabin and picked up the box carefully. Then he carried it across the corridor to his own cabin.

He went back across the corridor once more. In every cabin there was a notice with the words "Do Not Disturb" written on it in large letters. Salahadin took this notice and hung it on the door of cabin 22.

DO NOT DISTURB

The steward will see this on the door, thought Salahadin to himself. He'll think that Peterson is sick. No one will go into cabin 22 until Venice.

He locked the door of cabin 22 and put the key on its hook in the steward's room. Then Salahadin went back to his own cabin. The food was still on the table, but he was not hungry. He threw it out of the window.

Salahadin looked at his watch. He was surprised. It was only a quarter to nine. A lot had happened in a short time.

After a few minutes there was a knock at the door. It was the steward.

'I hope that you enjoyed your dinner, sir,' he said to Salahadin.

'Thank you,' replied Salahadin. 'I enjoyed it very much.'

'Mr Peterson's put the "Do Not Disturb" notice on his door,' said the steward. 'Perhaps he's sick. I'll not disturb him until Venice.'

'Yes,' said Salahadin. 'I met him half an hour ago. He said that he felt sick. He'll not want anything until tomorrow.'

'When do you want breakfast, sir?' asked the steward.

'I feel tired,' replied Salahadin. 'Don't wake me in the morning. When I want breakfast, I'll call you.'

'Goodnight, then,' said the steward.

Salahadin said goodnight and locked his door. He had not slept on a bed for many hours and he was very tired. He undressed and got into bed. At first, the movement of the boat kept him awake. But he was soon asleep and slept deeply all night.

When Salahadin woke up the next morning, the bright sun was shining into his cabin. He looked at his watch. It was nearly eleven o'clock. He rang the bell for the steward.

'When do we arrive in Venice?' asked Salahadin.

'We're early today,' replied the steward. 'We'll be there in two hours. But you don't need to get off the boat immediately. You can have lunch first.'

'No, thank you,' said Salahadin. 'I want to get off the boat as soon as possible. What about Mr Peterson? Is he better?'

'He still has the notice on his door,' replied the steward. 'I'll not disturb him until after lunch.'

'That's a good idea,' said Salahadin. 'Now, can you bring me some coffee, please.'

Salahadin drank his coffee slowly and got dressed. He heard a lot of noise. The ship was arriving at Venice.

Salahadin looked out into the corridor. It was empty. The steward had gone to the dining-room. Salahadin picked up the heavy box and left the cabin.

From the side of the boat, Salahadin saw the tall buildings

of Venice. They were passing in front of St Mark's Cathedral. They were now near the docks.

After half an hour, the boat was beside the dock. Salahadin left *The Syria* while the other passengers were having lunch.

'What's in that box?' asked a policeman.

'Some books,' replied Salahadin. He did not want any trouble.

The policeman did not ask Salahadin to open the box. In a few minutes, Salahadin was in a water taxi on his way to the railway station.

Safe at last, thought Salahadin. When they open cabin 22, they'll find it empty. They'll be very surprised.

14

Return to Cairo

Salahadin took the first train from Venice to Rome. The next morning he was on a plane for Cairo. The plane was late and he did not arrive until after ten o'clock in the morning.

The sun was high in the sky and it was getting hotter and hotter. Salahadin felt better. He preferred the heat of Cairo to the cold deck of *The Syria.*

He took a taxi to his flat. There was a surprise waiting for him. Leila and Fuad were there. Fuad explained.

'We arrived this morning from Beirut,' he said. 'We were worried about you. You didn't send a telegram. We thought that something had happened.'

'Of course, the telegram!' said Salahadin. 'I forgot to send you a telegram. I'm really sorry.'

'We phoned the police here in Cairo,' said Fuad. 'No one knew anything about you. We were very worried.'

'It's my fault,' said Salahadin.

He told them what had happened. They were happy that he was safe back in Cairo.

'And this is the box,' said Leila. 'The Black Cat is in this box. Let's open it.'

Salahadin opened the box and lifted out the Black Cat.

'It doesn't look very valuable,' said Leila. 'I don't like it at all.'

'We don't know its value,' said Salahadin. 'We'll take it to the Cairo Museum tomorrow.'

'Then you can have a holiday,' said Leila. 'You need a rest. Perhaps you'll show us round Cairo.'

'That won't be a rest,' replied Salahadin. 'But it's a good idea.'

'I'm going to make coffee,' said Leila. 'Do you both want some?'

'Yes, please,' replied Salahadin. 'I want some coffee and I want *your* story, Fuad. What happened at Ba'albek?' And Fuad told his story.

'I went to the Beirut police,' Fuad began, 'and told them about Borkman's death. They asked a lot of questions.'

'Police always ask a lot of questions,' said Salahadin.

'I told them about Peterson,' continued Fuad. 'And I said that you had gone to Athens.'

'Did they believe you?'

'Not at first,' replied Fuad. 'Then I told them about the Black Cat. I gave them Borkman's message. I told them about the café in Ba'albek and about Jusef. Then they believed me.'

'And what happened next?' asked Salahadin.

'The police asked me to help them,' replied Fuad. 'It wasn't possible for a policeman to go into Jusef's café. The people there knew all the policemen. Jusef was a clever man. The police had to trick him and they asked me to go to Ba'albek. They wanted me to go into the café and give Jusef the message from Borkman.

'I went to Ba'albek in the evening,' continued Fuad. 'I found Jusef's café. It was near the ruins of the old city. I sat down and asked for coffee. Then I asked for Jusef. I told Jusef about Borkman's death.

'The police were waiting outside,' Fuad continued. 'They were hiding in a car. I told Jusef about the Black Cat and he thanked me. Then he hurried out of the café.'

'And the police saw him?' asked Salahadin.

'Yes,' said Fuad. 'They watched him carefully.'

'Where did Jusef go?'

'He got into a car,' replied Fuad, 'and drove to a farm in the mountains. The police followed him. Then they hid in the hills round the farm and waited.'

'How many men were at the farm?' Salahadin asked.

'The police didn't know,' replied Fuad. 'They waited for more police. Then they shouted to the men at the farm and told them to come out.'

'Didn't the men at the farm shoot at the police?'

'No, they didn't,' replied Fuad. 'There were only three of them at the farm. Borkman was dead and Peterson was on *The Syria*. The three men came out without shooting. The police took them away. They're now in prison.'

'Did they catch the leader of the gang?' asked Salahadin.

'Jusef was the leader,' replied Fuad. 'He's now in prison with the others.'

'Jusef's in prison,' said Salahadin. 'Borkman's dead and so is Peterson. That's the end of the Ba'albek Gang.'

'And three of the Red Hand Gang were killed in the black car,' said Leila.

'That's true,' said Salahadin. 'We'll have no more trouble for some time.'

15

The End

The next morning Salahadin went with Leila and Fuad to the Cairo Museum. They took the Black Cat with them. They met a friend called Faisal who worked in the museum.

Salahadin gave the Black Cat to Faisal and told him the story.

'It looks old,' said Faisal, 'and perhaps it's valuable. But I don't know about the gold and diamonds. I'll have to look at it carefully.'

Salahadin, Leila and Fuad went and had some coffee. They came back to the museum about two hours later.

'Well, what's the answer?' asked Fuad.

'It's very old,' replied Faisal. 'But it's not made of gold and there are no diamonds. The eyes and collar are made of stone. The cat is made of a heavy kind of wood.'

'So, it isn't valuable,' said Leila. 'Seven men have died for a piece of wood.'

'No, you're wrong,' said Faisal. 'It's very, very valuable. It's more than two thousand years old. The gold and diamonds aren't important.'

'Perhaps there really was a gold cat,' said Salahadin. 'Perhaps tomb robbers stole the real cat thousands of years ago. Then they put this wooden cat into the tomb.'

'We'll never know,' said Fuad. 'But we're lucky to have this one.'

'Yes, we are lucky,' said Faisal. 'Can we have it for our museum?'

'Of course you can,' replied Salahadin. 'This is the right place for it.'

'Come back in November,' said Faisal. 'Then you'll see the Black Cat in its right place.'

'And we'll come back, too,' said Leila. 'Fuad's been working too hard. He needs a real holiday. We'll come back to Cairo for two weeks in November.'

'That's a good idea,' said Faisal. 'I'll see you all then.'

Six months later, Salahadin was sitting in his office. Summer was over and the weather was getting cool. The telephone rang.

'You remember your promise, don't you?' asked Faisal.

'My promise?'

'To come to the museum,' continued Faisal. 'The new room is going to be opened tomorrow at ten o'clock.'

'Oh – of course,' said Salahadin. 'I'll be there.'

The next morning, there was a crowd of people in the museum. Faisal met Salahadin and took him to the new room. There was a large notice outside the door.

THE TREASURES OF ANKUTEN

Archeologists had found the tomb of Ankuten. Pearson's map had helped them. They had brought many things from the tomb to Cairo. They were all in this room.

Ahmed was standing in the middle of the room. He was talking to Fuad and Leila. The taxi driver who had taken Borkman to Cairo station was there also. Salahadin went over to say hello.

'Do you see what's behind me?' asked Ahmed.

There, in the centre of the room, was a large glass case. The Black Cat was inside. Underneath, there was a notice:

The Black Cat of Ankuten
given by Salahadin El Nur

Ahmed was standing in the middle of the room. Salahadin went over to say hello.

POINTS FOR UNDERSTANDING

Points for Understanding

1

1 What was Salahadin's job?
2 What had Mr Pearson been doing in Egypt?
3 Why was Salahadin worried?
4 Why was Salahadin not able to speak to Mr Pearson?

2

1 What did Salahadin find on the table beside the bed?
2 How many boxes were in the room?
3 Which box was missing?

3

1 Did the man in the taxi speak Arabic like an Egyptian?
2 Where did the man want to go?
3 What train left Cairo at twelve o'clock, midday?

4

1 Who had arrived at Alexandria docks at six o'clock?
2 Why did the police not open the box?
3 What boats left Alexandria between 4.30 p.m. and 8.00 p.m.?
4 How was Salahadin going to travel to Beirut?

5

1 Which pieces of paper did Salahadin take out of his wallet?
2 What tomb was Pearson looking for?
3 What was possibly buried in this tomb?
4 Was it valuable?

6

1 What was the name of the boat which arrived at Beirut at half past six?
2 Where was Fuad's village?
3 Was it an easy road from Beirut to Fuad's village?

7

1 What was the name of the man who got off the boat?
2 Was the man carrying the box?
3 What happened when the taxi left the docks?
4 Which road did the cars take?
5 What happened to the black car and the taxi?

8

1 Where did Borkman ask Fuad and Salahadin to go?
2 Who was following Borkman and why?
3 Where was the Black Cat?
4 Why did Salahadin not want to wait for the police?

9

1 Who murdered Pearson?
2 How was Salahadin going to travel to Athens?
3 Why was Salahadin going to Athens?
4 What did Fuad ask Salahadin to do in Athens?

10

1 Why did Salahadin get on to *The Syria*?
2 Who was in cabin 22?
3 What was the number of Salahadin's cabin?

11

1 Why did Salahadin go into the steward's room?
2 Where did Salahadin find the missing box?
3 What went wrong?

12

1 Did Salahadin tell Peterson the truth?
2 What happened to Peterson?
3 Where was the Black Cat now?

13

1 Why did Salahadin put the "Do Not Disturb" notice on the door of cabin 22?
2 Why did Salahadin tell the policeman that he had some books in the box?

14

1 Where was Salahadin going to take the Black Cat?
2 Who was the leader of the Ba'albek Gang?
3 What had happened to the two gangs?

15

1 Was the Black Cat valuable?
2 What was inside the new room in the museum?

Exercises

Making Sentences

Put the words on the right in the correct order to complete the sentences.

1	Inspector Salahadin's job was	*to the Egypt of antiquities protect.*
	Inspector Salahadin's job was to protect the antiquities of Egypt.	
2	Mr Pearson was murdered because	of the Ankuten Black Cat found he.
	....	
3	Borkman killed Pearson and then	to Black Cat took the Alexandria.
	....	
4	Two ships left Alexandria	one to Beirut went and Athens one to.
	....	
5	*The Syria* sailed to Athens and	to Venice went then.
	....	
6	Borkman was killed	in Ba'albek near a crash car.
	....	
7	Salahadin flew from Beirut to Athens	and got to Venice on the ship.
	....	
8	Peterson had the Black Cat	in *The Syria* onboard number 22 cabin.
	....	
9	Salahadin took the Black Cat to Egypt	and put the Museum Cairo in it.
	....	

Words From the Story

Unjumble the letters to find words from the story. The meanings are given to help you.

1 **lishagerocot**
Meaning: a person who studies very old buildings and objects that are found in them
archeologist
....

2 **amonunit**
Meaning: a very high hill

....

3 **laveyl**
Meaning: low land, often with a river, between hills or mountains

....

4 **horapah**
Meaning: a king of ancient Egypt

....

5 **sirun**
Meaning: old buildings that are badly damaged

....

6 **labelvau**
Meaning: worth a lot of money

....

7 **donadim**
Meaning: a hard stone that looks like clear glass and is valuable

....

8 **redwast**
Meaning: a person who serves food and drink on a ship or plane

....

Story Outline 1

Complete the gaps. Use each word in the box once.

ancient ~~Egyptian~~ archeologist of Cairo ruins more
the these not out an made and was
murdered for came to tell

Salahadin was an [1]......*Egyptian*...... police inspector. He worked [2].................. the Department [3]............. Antiquities in [4]...................................... .

Many archeologists [5]................................. to Egypt. They studied the [6]................................. and tombs of [7].. Egypt. These ruins were [8] .... than two thousand years old.

All archeologists had [9]............. go to [10].................. Department of Antiquities. They had to [11]....................................... Inspector Salahadin about their work. They could [12].................. take Egyptian antiquities [13].................. of the country.

Many of [14]...................................... antiquities were very valuable. There was [15]............. international black market in stolen antiquities.

The Black Cat of Ankuten [16].................. very valuable. People thought it was [17]......................... of gold and diamonds.

Pearson was an [18].. . He found the Black Cat [19].................. he took it to the Nile Hotel.

Pearson was [20].. and the Black Cat was stolen.

Story Outline 2

foreigner talked had found driver carrying hotel near station followed remembered Arabic did boat sailed decided tomb contained statue why

At first, Inspector Salahadin [1].......................... not know [2]........................... Pearson was murdered. He [3].. to the hotel staff. Two porters [4].. that Pearson [5]......................... seven boxes. But Salahadin [6].................................... only six boxes in Pearson's [7].. room.

A taxi [8].. had picked up a foreigner [9]......................... the hotel. The foreigner was [10]... a heavy box. The taxi driver took the [11]... to the railway [12].. . He said that the foreigner spoke [13]................................. with a Lebanese accent.

Salahadin thought that the foreigner had gone to Alexandria. A boat, called *The Sudan*, [14]... to Beirut that evening. A second [15]... , called *The Syria*, sailed to Athens. Salahadin [16].. to go to Beirut. He flew to Lebanon.

What was in the box? Pearson left notes about the [17]...................................... of Pharaoh Ankuten. Ankuten had loved black cats. Salahadin thought that the box [18]... a statue of a cat. It was a pharaoh's statue. It was very valuable.

The foreigner, called Borkman, went to Beirut but the [19].. of the black cat went to Athens. Salahadin [20]...................................... the statue to Greece. Then he sailed on *The Syria* from Athens to Venice.

Choose the Verb

Complete the gaps with the correct verb form from the brackets.

The corridor outside cabin 22 [1]**(was / were)** ....*was*.............. still empty. Everything [2]**(was / were)** .... silent. Salahadin [3]**(was going / went)** .... into the cabin and [4]**(picked up / was picking up)** .... the box carefully. Then he [5]**(carries / carried)** .... it across the corridor to his own cabin.

He [6]**(goes / went)** .... back across the corridor once more. In every cabin there [7]**(was / were)** .... a notice with the words "Do Not Disturb" [8]**(wrote / written)** .... on it in large letters. Salahadin [9]**(takes / took)** .... this notice and [10]**(hanged / hung)** .... it on the door of cabin 22.

The steward [11]**(will see / is seeing)** .... this on the door, [12]**(is thinking / thought)** .... Salahadin to himself. He [13]**(will think / is thinking)** .... that Peterson [14]**(was / is)** .... sick. No one [15]**(will go / has gone)** .... into cabin 22 until the ship [16]**(will reach / reaches)** .... Venice.

He [17]**(locked / was locking)** .... the door of cabin 22 and [18]**(putting / put)** .... the key on its hook in the steward's room. Then Salahadin [19]**(goes / went)** .... back to his own cabin. The food [20]**(was / were)** .... still on the table, but he [21]**(was / were)** .... not hungry. He [22]**(was throwing / threw)** .... it out of the window.

After a few minutes the steward [23]**(knocked / has knocked)** .... on the door. 'I [24]**(have been hoping / hope)** .... you [25]**(enjoy / enjoyed)** .... your dinner, sir,' he [26]**(said / will say)** .... to Salahadin.

True or False?

Read the sentence. Then write T (True) or F (False) next to the statements below.

1 Borkman spoke Lebanese Arabic but he had a Swedish passport.

a [T] He spoke Arabic like a man from Lebanon.

b [F] He sounded like an Egyptian.

c [F] His nationality was Lebanese.

d [T] He did not have a Lebanese passport.

2 All archeologists had to report to Salahadin's office before they left Egypt, but Pearson did not come. Salahadin thought there might be a problem. He called the Nile Hotel.

a [ ] Pearson was not an archeologist.

b [ ] Salahadin was waiting for Pearson.

c [ ] Salahadin did not know where Pearson was staying.

d [ ] Salahadin was worried about Pearson.

3 Salahadin spoke to the hotel porters. They said Pearson had seven boxes when he came to the hotel, but Salahadin found only six in the dead man's room.

a [ ] There were six boxes in Pearson's room.

b [ ] The seventh box was missing.

c [ ] Salahadin asked Pearson about the missing box.

d [ ] The porters saw Pearson's seven boxes.

4 Pearson was murdered at about ten thirty in the morning. He was stabbed with a knife, and his body was found in his hotel room.

a [ ] Pearson was shot dead.

b [ ] He was at home when he was killed.

c [ ] He died in the afternoon.

d [ ] He was staying at a hotel when he died.

5 A taxi driver took a foreigner to the railway station from the Nile Hotel. The foreigner was carrying a heavy box. The taxi driver told Salahadin about the man.

a ☐ The foreigner probably caught a train.
b ☐ Salahadin spoke to a train driver.
c ☐ The driver said the man with the box was Egyptian.
d ☐ The box was very light.

6 You need a passport to travel to another country. Salahadin went to Lebanon and Greece by plane and to Italy by ship.

a ☐ Salahadin had a passport.
b ☐ He went to Italy by plane.
c ☐ He sailed to Greece from Lebanon.
d ☐ He flew to Lebanon.

Word Focus: *inspector*

An *inspector* a person whose job is to make sure that things are done correctly.

Read the descriptions below. Then complete the gaps using the words in the box.

~~police~~ ticket health customs school tax inspector

1 Salahadin's makes sure that crimes are investigated. He looks for criminals.
He's a *police inspector* ....

2 This person works at an airport or sea port. He/She makes sure that no one brings illegal things into the country. He/She looks for drugs and guns.
He/She's a ....

3 This person works on buses, trains or trams. He/She makes sure that everyone buys a ticket. He/She looks for people who do not have a ticket.
He/She's a ....

4 This person works for the Ministry of Education. He/She goes to schools to make sure they are doing things properly. He/She looks for bad teachers.
He/She's a ....

5 This person works for the Ministry of Finance. He/She makes sure that everyone pays their taxes. He/She looks for people who do not pay their taxes.
He/She's a ....

6 This person works for the Ministry of Public Health. He/She makes sure that hospitals and restaurants are clean. He/She looks for dirty public places.
He/She's a ....

Dictionary: *- spect -*

Write each word from the box next to the correct meaning.

inspect	inspection	spectacles	spectacle	spectator	spectacular

1 Meaning: wonderful or amazing to see
spectacular
....

2 Meaning: glasses you wear over your eyes to help you to see
....

3 Meaning: a person who watches something that is happening
....

4 Meaning: a careful or official check

....

5 Meaning: to look at something carefully

....

6 Meaning: a big show that people watch for entertainment

....

The 'root' of these words is *–spect-*. What do you think it means?

....

Look in your dictionary or think of other words with the root *–spect-*.

....

What Happened Next?

Number the sentences in the correct order to give the outline of the story.

- [ ] Borkman killed Pearson.
- [ ] Pearson took the Black Cat to Cairo.
- [ ] He found the Black Cat inside the tomb of Ankuten.
- [ ] He found the tomb of Pharaoh Ankuten.
- [ ] Salahadin found the Black Cat in the shower-room in Peterson's cabin.
- [*1*] Pearson went digging in the Valley of Zar.
- [ ] Peterson sailed to Athens and on towards Venice.
- [ ] Borkman gave the Black Cat to Peterson.
- [ ] He took the Black Cat to Alexandria.
- [ ] Salahadin killed Peterson.

Published by Macmillan Heinemann ELT
Between Towns Road, Oxford OX4 3PP
Macmillan Heinemann ELT is an imprint of
Macmillan Publishers Limited
Companies and representatives throughout the world
Heinemann is a registered trademark of Harcourt Education, used under licence.

ISBN 978–0–2300–2923–1

First published 1975

This edition first published 2007

Illustrated by Peter Edwards
Original cover template design by Jackie Hill
Cover photography by Alamy/Pix

Printed in Thailand

2011 2010 2009 2008 2007
9 8 7 6 5 4 3 2 1